Hiya,

I am not the world's greatest cook. Soups and stews sizzle and burn, soufflés sink, pies darken and dry out until the pastry is tougher than old shoe leather. Cakes, though . . . that's a different story. If I'm baking, I do not get bored and wander off. I browse through the recipes and look at the pictures, and mix and taste and measure. I love messing about with little cake cases, I love licking the leftover cake mix, I love slathering on thick drifts of icing and adding sprinkles or icing sugar or a juicy strawberry on top.

Most of all, though, I love testing out the results! Cakes are cool . . . even if they are homemade and a little bit wonky! I think you'll have fun trying out the recipes in this mini-book – and sharing them with your friends! Make a few batches and hand them out randomly at school . . . guaranteed to make people smile!

While we're talking things-that-make-you-smile, we've got the low-down on boys, all you need to know to make your own cool magazine and a brand-new mini-story, a kind of 'taster', if you like, for my brand-new book Angel Cake. I think you'll like it . . . notice a bit of a cake theme going on, anyone?!!!

Remember . . . life is sweet!

Best Wishes,

Cathy Cassidy
x

Books by Cathy Cassidy

DIZZY

DRIFTWOOD

INDIGO BLUE

LUCKY STAR

SCARLETT

SUNDAE GIRL

GINGERSNAPS

Look out for

ANGEL CAKE

cathy cassidy

Cupcakes & Kisses

PUFFIN

PUFFIN BOOKS

Published by the Penguin Group

Penguin Books Ltd, 80 Strand, London WC2R 0RL, England

Penguin Group (USA) Inc., 375 Hudson Street, New York, New York 10014, USA

Penguin Group (Canada), 90 Eglinton Avenue East, Suite 700, Toronto, Ontario, Canada
M4P 2Y3 (a division of Pearson Penguin Canada Inc.)

Penguin Ireland, 25 St Stephen's Green, Dublin 2, Ireland (a division of Penguin Books Ltd)

Penguin Group (Australia), 250 Camberwell Road, Camberwell, Victoria 3124, Australia
(a division of Pearson Australia Group Pty Ltd)

Penguin Books India Pvt Ltd, 11 Community Centre, Panchsheel Park,
New Delhi – 110 017, India

Penguin Group (NZ), 67 Apollo Drive, Rosedale, North Shore 0632, New Zealand
(a division of Pearson New Zealand Ltd)

Penguin Books (South Africa) (Pty) Ltd, 24 Sturdee Avenue, Rosebank,
Johannesburg 2196, South Africa

Penguin Books Ltd, Registered Offices: 80 Strand, London WC2R 0RL, England

puffinbooks.com

First published 2009
1

Made and printed in England by Clays Ltd, St Ives plc

ISBN: 978–0–141–32918–5

Contents

Lily's Story   1

About Cathy   12

Let's Hear It for the Boys!   18

Boys Allowed!   21

Make a Mag!!!!   22

Best Friends' Day   30

Party, Party!   31

Hold Your Own Friendship Festival   33

Angel Cake Heaven   34

Finn's Fantastic Choc 'n' Orange Cupcakes   35

Indigo's Blueberry Muffins   36

Cathy's Sticky Caramel Cupcakes   37

Scarlett's Scrumptious Banana Walnut Muffins   38

Cat's Crazy Carrot Muffins   39

Cathy Cassidy's Dream Flags   40

Random Acts of Kindness   42

Cathy Cassidy Quiz Time   48

Letters to Cathy   50

Cathy's new book

Angel Cake

is all about Polish girl Anya, who comes to Britain and finds it a whole lot harder to settle than she imagined . . . until she falls for cute bad-boy Dan. The book is written from Anya's point of view, but this mini-story, linked to the book, is seen through the eyes of mean-girl Lily Caldwell, who takes an instant dislike to Anya . . .

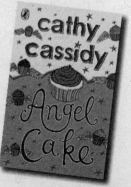

Just what is Lily's problem?

Lily's Story

I hated Anya Mikalski from the first moment I saw her. Everything about her made my lip curl . . . her long blonde hair, her creamy skin, her big blue eyes that looked like they might brim with tears at any moment.

She looked terrified. St Peter and Paul's High School can be a crazy place, and I didn't envy her, walking into class in the middle of the autumn term, not knowing a word of English.

Someone should have told her that Scared Rabbit is not a good look here.

She was flavour of the month for a while, of course. She was Polish, and the girls thought her accent was cute, while the boys thought she was exotic and beautiful. Everyone wanted to be her friend at first, but that didn't last long. Anya was silent and scared and sad-eyed, and sometimes she looked at us as if we were a pack of wild animals.

Before long, people started saying that she was stuck-up, stand-offish, that she didn't want to fit in. They lost interest, and then Anya was on her own.

I knew how she felt. I could see she wasn't stuck-up or stand-offish, she was just way out of her depth, the way I once was. I could have helped her, but I didn't. Why should I? Nobody helped me.

I had to learn by my mistakes, find a place for myself. I wasn't about to lose that, not for someone like Anya.

Pretty soon, she faded into the background, and the only people who bothered with her with the losers and the geeks.

Well, fine. They were welcome to her.

Every school has its misfits, right? The kids that stand out from the crowd, the weird ones, the nerdy, needy ones. Sometimes they look odd, like Kurt Jones with those dodgy crimpline trousers that flap around his ankles and Frances McGee who thinks it's OK to wear fishnet tights and black lace miniskirts even though she is the size of a small whale. Other times, they look OK, pretty even, like Anya Mikalski, but, still, they don't fit in.

Kids have a radar for anyone who seems shy or lost or vulnerable, and if you show up on that radar, they can make your life a misery.

I should know.

Back in primary school, I was one of the misfits.

I never quite worked out how it happened . . . I wasn't geeky, I wasn't weird, and I don't think I was ugly either. I just seemed to have an invisible sign on my head that invited other kids to wind me up. I had zero confidence, and they could see that.

I wanted to be liked – who doesn't? I always had quite a bit of pocket money, and I used to buy sweets on the way into school to share with my classmates. I thought that would make them like me, but it didn't. They just ate the sweets and laughed at me and left me standing at the side of the playground alone.

'You can't play right now, Lily,' they'd explain. 'We have enough people already. Maybe tomorrow?'

It was the same when someone had a birthday. They'd hand round invitations on bright printed paper, one for almost everyone. Everyone except me. 'I can only have twelve people,' a girl called Sophie Ford once explained to me. 'Mum said. But if anyone drops out, or can't make it, then of course you can come too, Lily. I'd like you to be there really.'

I knew it was mean, but I prayed that one of the others would be ill so there'd be a space for me to go to the party, and sure enough, two days before, Lindsay Ashton got tonsillitis. I told my mum I was going to the party, and she raised an eyebrow and said it was about time I made some friends.

'You're such an odd little thing,' she said. 'I always had lots of friends, when I was your age. Sometimes, I think you try too hard. You're like an overenthusiastic puppy. It can be irritating, Lily.'

What are you supposed to do when your own mum thinks you're irritating? My eyes blurred with tears, but Mum just shook her head and handed me a tenner to buy a present for Sophie Ford. I added some of my pocket money to it and bought a Bratz doll, because we were only nine back then and I knew Sophie collected them.

On the day of the party, Lindsay Ashton was still off ill, and I couldn't keep the smile off my face. I handed over the present and Sophie loved it, just like I knew she would. 'Wow, Lily!' she said. 'This is amazing! You shouldn't have! It must have cost loads!'

'Well, we're friends, aren't we?' I grinned.

'Yeah,' Sophie echoed. 'Sure . . . friends.'

At last, I would be accepted. I'd be one of the gang.

Sophie was nice to me all day, but at home-time she took me aside and explained she really wished she could ask me to the party instead of Lindsay, but it just wasn't possible. 'I already asked Kayla Bennett yesterday. I promised her. Sorry, Lily.'

My world fell apart. I sat on the swings in the park for three hours that day, so I could pretend to Mum and Dad I'd been at the party. When I came in, they were drinking wine with their friends and talking about work stuff, but Mum looked up as I came in, checking her watch as if surprised and faintly annoyed to see me back so soon. 'I didn't make you any tea, Lily,' she said. 'I knew you'd fill up on party food and crisps and cake. Run along, now.'

I remember sneaking bread and cheese from the fridge and crying myself to sleep.

Well, all that was a long time ago, of course. Girls can be mean, right? They have these invisible rules about who fits in and who doesn't, and after a while I realized I never, ever would. I tried not to care. I hung out with the boys after that, with Dan Carney and his friends. They shared my sweets, just like the girls had, but they let me hang out with them at break-times too. They were loud and funny and often in trouble, but they didn't seem to mind having me around.

High school was a fresh start, and I was determined not to waste it. Mum took me shopping for uniform, and I made sure we went to the right shops, bought short skirts and high-heeled boots and a little blue jumper that showed off my new curves.

I wanted to look cool, grown-up.

I watched as the girls from my old primary formed new friendships, new alliances. Everyone had a chance to make friends here, even me, but I realized I just didn't know how. I was out of practice, and I knew a bag of sweets wouldn't get me too far in this place.

Once, in the first week, that plump, weird goth-girl Frances McGee came up to me in English class and asked if she could sit by me. I could see Sophie Ford and the cool girls in the class watching, curious to see what I would do.

I wanted to tell Frances she could sit down, sure. She looked friendly and fun, and I kind of admired her confidence for dressing the way she wanted to even though she was overweight. But I knew that if I settled for being one of the misfit gang, I'd never be anything more.

'I don't think so,' I told Frances, and a little spark of power flared inside of me as I saw her face fall. Power . . . that was a new feeling. It made me brave, it made me mean. 'There's no room,' I said to Frances, looking her up and down. 'If you know what I mean.'

A couple of the kids behind me giggled, and even Sophie smiled. Frances blushed and flumped into a seat at the back of the class, and I pushed away my guilt because it actually felt good to be the one in control, the one who could pick and choose. I discovered that if you can't fit in, you can at least act like you don't care, like you're too mean and cool to need anyone at all.

And of course, I still had the boys.

Dan was always in trouble back at primary,

but not serious trouble. He was the kind of kid the teachers liked, cheeky but smart, and he could talk his way out of most tricky situations. It was different at St Peter and Paul's. The teachers had no patience for jokes and backchat, and Dan quickly got himself a bad reputation. His friends were the other bad boys: lazy, careless, hoody-clad kids who listened to rap music and sometimes shared stolen ciggies round the back of the gym block.

I started taking the odd ciggy from Mum's handbag or pocketing half-empty packets whenever I could so I could hang out with the boys by the gym block and maybe offer them a ciggy now and again. I didn't mean to get hooked, but pretty soon I was, and I told myself I didn't care. I got used to the taste of tobacco and stale smoke, the faint stain of yellow on my fingers.

I was part of the gang.

After all, I was a bad girl myself now. The days of trying too hard, of being puppy-dog-eager-to-please, were long gone. I developed a sharp tongue, a quick wit, a nice line in put-downs. I saw respect, or maybe fear, in the eyes of my classmates, and it felt a whole lot better than pity.

'You've changed,' Dan said to me, and I couldn't

work out if he meant for the better or not. Dan was a natural rebel, but he had a kind streak too. He gave the teachers a whole lot of grief, but he didn't smoke, and he was never, ever mean. I knew he didn't like bullies.

'Everyone changes,' I told him, looking at him from under my lashes. 'It's called growing up.'

'Maybe,' Dan said, frowning. 'But don't change too much, Lily. Remember the way things used to be.'

If anyone else had said that to me, I'd have been mad. What right did anyone have to tell me how to behave? I knew exactly what it felt like to be on the outside, and it wasn't good. Being cool and mean was a whole lot better, trust me. But I liked Dan, I liked him a lot, and so I just shrugged and smiled and told him I was still the same person, underneath, and after that, I tried not to be too bitchy when Dan was around.

I hoped that some day he'd look at me in a way that was more than just friendly. I even dated a few of his hoody-boy mates, but that didn't work out too well. Every time things got past the hand-holding stage it was like wrestling with an octopus, and that's not a whole lot of fun, seriously, so things tended to fizzle out pretty fast. And Dan still didn't notice me.

He didn't seem interested in girls at all, until Anya Mikalski came along. He fell for her, big style. I saw it all, the way his dark eyes softened when he looked at her, the way his cool, couldn't-care-less mouth curved into a secret smile whenever she was around.

That's why I hated Anya Mikalski. I looked at her pale-blonde hair and big blue eyes and I wanted to slap her, because Dan was crushing on her and she didn't even know it.

She was too wrapped up in trying to keep her head above water, trying to survive. Well, too bad. She was never going to be one of the cool kids with her geeky friends and her sad little accent, whatever Dan might think. I wished she'd go back to wherever she came from, back to Poland – to the land of beetroot soup and sauerkraut and whatever else they eat over there . . . anywhere, really, as long as it was a million miles from Dan.

But Dan had other ideas.

And that's where the trouble began . . .

Want to find out what happens between
Anya and Dan . . . and how Lily fits in?
Read *Angel Cake*, out now!

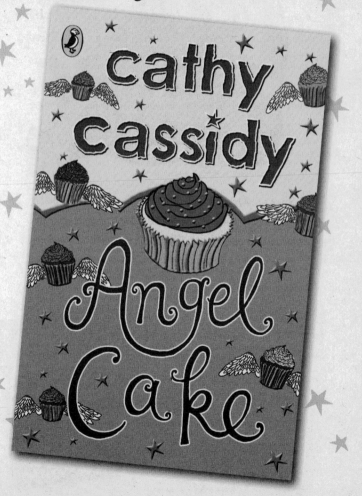

About Cathy

Photo: Chris Watt

We know Cathy is a fabulous writer, but she's many other things too! We chose ten ways to describe Cathy and asked her to tell us about each one. So, Cathy, it's over to you . . .

Author

Dizzy, my first book, was published five years ago, so being an author still feels pretty new to me! It's what I've always dreamed of, so it's a great feeling to know that dreams really can come true! There are LOTS of books out there now, and plenty more in the pipeline . . . so keep reading!

Artist

After school, I went to **art college** and trained to be an **illustrator**. I LOVED it. I freelanced as an illustrator for a long time. I don't design my own covers for the books – that's a fab Puffin artist called Sara Flavell – but I did do all the illustrations and cover for my new, younger series, *Daizy Star*. That was a lot of fun!!! I am always doodling pics of characters when thinking up new plots and storylines!

Wife and mum

I have a fab and very supportive **husband, Liam** . . . he's lots of fun and does most of the cooking and never, ever steals my chocolate! We have **two children, Cal and Caitlin**, who are teenagers now. They are really into music and are in a band with their friends, so life at home can be pretty chaotic these days! I miss my family like mad when I am touring away from home . . .

Chocaholic

Chocolate . . . sigh!!! I love chocolate and friends have called me a **chocolate addict** since I was a kid . . . oops!!! I just love the way it melts in your mouth and makes you feel all happy and floaty . . . and yes, I know you are supposed to like the healthy, organic one hundred per cent dark sort, because it's good for you, but sadly I much prefer the not-so-healthy, sugary, milk-chocolate kind. My faves are **Thorntons truffles** and **Terry's chocolate oranges** . . . heaven!!!

Former teacher

I have been an **art teacher** in both high schools and primaries for a long time, and loved it . . . teaching is cool! I like helping kids to be the best artists they can be, and always felt really buzzed at how brilliant they were . . . art teaching is a LOT of fun. When I put a scatty art teacher, Miss Quinn, into my book **Driftwood**, my friends all thought the character was me . . . I guess I was a bit like that! One of the best things about teaching was that it helped me to understand young people a whole lot better . . . Kids have an **enthusiasm** and **energy** that often fades as we get older, and I find that enthusiasm really inspiring.

Animal lover

I have a collection of dodgy pets, I admit! There are two dogs: **Daisy**, a retired racing greyhound, and **Kelpie**, another 'rescue' dog – a mad, hairy lurcher who looks a bit like a toilet brush crossed with a kangaroo. She was the inspiration behind Leggit in *Dizzy* and *Lucky Star*! Then there are three 'rescue' cats – **Pickle**, **Lily** and **Pepper** –who inspired the kittens in *Driftwood*! Last but not least, there are two 'rescue' rabbits: **Snowy**, who is white and elegant, and **Midnight**, who has only one eye and keeps bumping into things! They live on a big, fenced-in bit of bank, and they are kind of 'free-range', although they do have a hutch they can hide out in if they need to.

I went **veggie** when I was fourteen because I didn't like the idea of eating animals, and I do have strong feelings about the way we treat animals . . . **I hate animal cruelty.** I'd love to have an animal sanctuary one day, or maybe just a couple of pet llamas, some ducks, chickens, a donkey and maybe the odd goat or two . . . cool!

Best friend

I have two best friends, **Helen** and **Sheena**. They are very different, but they are both fun, clever, talented and caring. I know that if I was in trouble they'd always be there for me. They both live a long way away from me, which means that when we do get together it's kind of special! I have maybe ten or fifteen more very close friends too, and a whole raft of others who help to keep me sane and make life fun!

Friendship is ultra-important to me, and those friends have been collected slowly over the years. I didn't always find friends who were the 'perfect fit' for me back at school, but after a while I realized that the more you put into a friendship, the more you get out. Good friends can **inspire** you, understand you and help you when things get tough . . . and you know what? **That's better than chocolate!**

Bookworm

I love **reading**. We didn't have a whole lot of books in the house when I was growing up, but my dad would take me to the local libraries a couple of times a week and we'd come home with armfuls of books! **Libraries** are cool, as you can take a risk and pick out books you'd never normally buy . . . after all, if you don't like it, you just have to return it, and nobody minds! I have a LOT of books in my house these days, and teen books are my favourites . . . there are some amazing books out there for young people. I love the feeling of opening a book and **escaping into a whole different world**! I'm quite a fast reader, and if I'm really busy or away on tour, I'll actually set my alarm a little earlier so I can still squeeze an hour of reading into my day!

Agony aunt

I was the agony aunt for a young teen-mag for twelve years. It's a tough job, but one that really matters . . . growing up can be a tricky time, and if you can't talk to your parents about whatever is bothering you, it helps to have someone else to turn to. Now that I've stopped doing the magazine problem page, I actually get more letters and emails than ever before from kids who identify with characters or situations in my books and who feel that I can understand and help them. Although I can't send personal replies to everyone, I try to help by having a **Cathy Cassidy and ChildLine page** on my website, full of helpful advice for my readers. Watch out for a new non-fiction book, *Letters to Cathy*, too, answering some of the most frequently asked questions from troubled teens . . . it's a guide to life for young people, and **packed with help and advice**.

Daydreamer

I'd say **daydreaming** is my best skill . . . I've spent years practising and perfecting my technique (mostly in school maths lessons, but let's not dwell on that!). Daydreaming started out for me as a way of making up stories in my head so that I could escape from a dull lesson, but it's turned into much more than that . . . it's the way all of my books start out. An idea catches my **imagination**, and I daydream about it, creating characters and plots and dramatic moments as part of the daydream . . . Try it, **it's addictive**! I think daydreaming can be very **creative** and can really help a story come to life. When kids email me and say things like, 'I felt like I was IN the story,' I know they can see the daydream as vividly as I could! Now that I am a published writer, I guess I get to daydream for a living . . . how cool is that?

17

Let's Hear It for the Boys!

There are some utterly swoonsome, completely heartmelting and totally gorgeous boys in Cathy's books. Take our Cupcakes and Kisses Test to find out if you're head over heels for Sam, daydreaming over Dan or crazy about Kian . . .

1 Have you ever had a crush on a boy with:

   A Long floppy hair?

   B Tangled curly hair?

   C Funky, trendy hair?

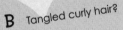

2 Would your ideal boy be:

   A Mysterious and secretive?

   B Weird and wonderful?

   C Rebellious and cool?

3 If you could gaze dreamily into a boy's eyes, would they be:

   A Dark and shining?

   B Bright and twinkly?

   C The colour of melted chocolate?

4 **What is your idea of a fab first date?**

A   A moonlit horse ride

B   An early morning narrowboat trip

C   A midnight bicycle tour (complete with cupcakes)

5 **Which of these talents would your dream boy have?**

A   Making magic

B   Making music

C   Making mischief

6 **Which of these would make a dreamy first impression on you?**

A   A luscious lilting accent

B   The sound of a saxophone

C   A big cheeky grin

7 **Which look would you most prefer for your dream guy?**

A   Frayed jeans and braided bracelets

B   Trilby hat and Converse

C   Baggy trousers and designer-label hoodies

Mostly  As

You're crazy for the **KIAN** type – those boys who seem a little bit mysterious and secretive. He's a bit of a risk-taker and believes that wishes really can come true, he's got a talent for making magical things happen and for making you feel safe and special.

Mostly  Bs

A boy like **SAM** is your type of guy. He's someone who dares to be different and doesn't follow rules. He's really into his music and doesn't care what people think – and will do everything he can to make you smile over a glass of blue lemonade.

Mostly  Cs

You've got a thing for bad boys like **DAN**. Dan is a bit of a rebel, he acts tough and pretends not to care. But really, there's a soft and gentle side to him, you just have to look beyond the mischief to see it. Deep down he's kind and sweet, he'd do anything for his mum – and for you!

BOYS Allowed!

It's mostly girls who read my books . . . or is it?
Who says that boys don't want to read real-life,
growing-up stories about friendship, families and
falling in love? Boys have friends, families and feelings
too, after all! Here's what the boys have to say . . .

JAMES SAYS . . .
Hi, I'm a boy and I love your
books. I read *Dizzy* first and
then I read *Scarlett* and *Indigo
Blue*. I had the whole series
for Christmas (apart from
GingerSnaps) and I bought
GingerSnaps two weeks ago in
a bookshop.

CONNOR SAYS . . .
I got your newsletter about
the boys and, well, I'd just like
to say that your books rock!
I think they're great and you
should never stop writing!

LUKE SAYS . . .
I love Cathy Cassidy's books,
especially *Driftwood* because
I think that Paul is very
sophisticated and unusual.

JAKE SAYS . . .
Why should I read
about war and football
all the time when I am
interested in girls, and
the books talk about
that and boys' books
don't. I get my girlfriend
to loan me the books
these days.

JAMIE SAYS . . .
My sister first introduced me to
your books and at first, seeing
Dizzy's bright pink cover, I
wasn't so sure, but after reading
the first page I was hooked.
People who say boys don't
read books don't know a thing!

KIERAN SAYS . . .
OK, I know I am in a minority
here but who cares. I have
read *Lucky Star* and I really
liked it. It's a lot more real to
life than stuff like underage
spies and SAS soldiers.

MAKE A MAG!!!!

Ever wished you could make your own mag, like the kids in *GingerSnaps*? Here's how!

FIND YOUR TEAM!

You can do a mag on your own if you have enough ideas, inspiration and time . . . but it's fun to have a team to work with! You need all kinds of people to make it cool . . .

Dreamers – they're the people with all the best ideas

Writers – to do the written bits!

Artists – to do lettering, graphics, illustrations, manga, etc

Digi photographers – pics of real people will make your mag come to life!

Organized people – to edit, plan and chase overdue features, etc

Confident people – to get adverts, arrange cool comps with local businesses and decide how/when to sell the mag

Nosy people!!! – they make the world's best investigative reporters . . . They can get out there and unearth the teachers' dark secrets!!!

BE PREPARED . . .

Set a date for your first meeting and invite a friendly teacher/librarian to help things run smoothly. Ask people to:

★ Bring along a couple of their fave magazines

★ Make a list of ideas for the mag

★ Choose some possible mag names

★ List their skills/interests/strengths

★ Think about the kind of jobs they'd like to do

FIRST MEETING!

★ Get people to talk about what THEY would like to see in the magazine – the more varied it is, the more people it will appeal to.

★ Decide WHO you will sell the mag to, and right from the start, think about them and what they might want.

★ Choose a name. Jot suggestions down, and vote for a favourite.

★ Divide up jobs. People can do a bit of everything, but it helps if you have one person to be in charge of certain things . . .

THE ED

will be someone organized – to plan, edit, chase up missing pages, make sure pages are laid out and passed on to be printed/copied.

ART ED

will be someone creative to design a fab cover, make sure every page looks great, and to produce posters to advertise the mag.

ADVERTISING ED

will be someone confident and good at maths, who will ask local businesses to place ads to raise money and help your mag cover its costs.

The eds might be doing other things too, but they have the final say about certain things. Choose people with the right skills for these jobs . . . or, if you prefer, do it all yourself!

The rest of the team can choose from the following, or be more than one thing . . . How about . . . reporter/journalist, artist, designer, agony aunt, photographer, writer, illustrator, reviewer . . . or anything else you can think of!!!

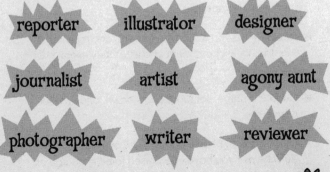

reporter   illustrator   designer

journalist   artist   agony aunt

photographer   writer   reviewer

IDEAS!

Leaf through some of your fave mags, jot ideas down and discuss.

You might choose to have . . .

* An interview with a local celeb/sports-star/musician/writer
* Photo interviews with kids in your school (if you include real pupils in your mag, more people will buy it!)
* Teacher features (fun, inspiring or embarrassing . . . you choose!)
* Features about fave interests/hobbies
* A letters page
* A problem page (use false names or make it a 'spoof' problem page)
* A fashion spread
* A sports feature
* A makeover (of the head? of the dinner ladies? of the kids?)
* A poster (some original artwork?)
* A competition or puzzles/Suduko
* A short story
* A quiz
* A jokes page
* Book/film/computer games/CD reviews
* Anything else you can think of!!!

STILL STUCK?

Photo interviews . . . a survey on school dinners/ uniform/where people are going on hols/what people want for Xmas/fave hobbies/fave subjects/what new reception or P1 kids think of the school, or what Year Seven or S1 kids think of secondary . . . or anything else you can think of! Take some digi photos of the people you interview and arrange these on the page with quotes beside . . .

Teacher features . . . run a comp to see if pupils can recognize teachers from their baby/childhood photos, ask teachers to describe their most embarrassing moments or run a quiz to match teachers to their fave hobbies/bands/books . . .

Features . . . in-depth photo features about cool hobbies, photo reports about events in school like World Book Day where kids dress as their fave fictional characters, non-uniform days, theatre visits, trips, etc.

Fashion . . . redesign the school uniform like Shannon in *GingerSnaps* . . . create some recycled fashion . . . go futuristic . . . the sky's the limit!

Decide who is doing what, and give everyone a deadline to hand in their finished work all neatly printed out.

PLAN IT ...

Sounds like a yawn, but unless you plan, you won't have a clue what goes where in the mag . . . or be able to keep track of what's been handed in, what still has to be done and which spaces need to be filled at the last minute . . .

Decide how many pages your mag will have and make a 'dummy' mag from plain A4 sheets . . . it should look like a blank white scrapbook! As each page is finished, photocopy it into the 'dummy' mag. As it builds up, you will be able to see what your mag will look like – and spot any gaps!

Decide on a price! Charge at least £1 for a twelve- or sixteen-page mag . . . affordable, but not too cheap!!! This will help cover printing costs.

ART ED ...

The art ed makes sure the mag looks cool! Decide whether to have a colour cover (depends on whether your school has access to a colour copier!). The inside is best left as black and white, unless you have unlimited funds!

The cover If your mag has a theme, i.e. Christmas, Jonas Brothers, fashion, that can be a starting point for your design . . . try a shot of the head in a Santa hat for a Christmas issue, or a painting of a Christmas tree! If it doesn't have a theme, try taking one of the features as inspiration . . . a pic from your fashion shoot or a cool manga drawing by the quiet, arty girl in Year Eight? Get thinking . . . get creating!

Use lettering that stands out, or pick out a font from your computer. And don't forget to put the price on!

For the **inside pages**, use cut and paste to create your pages. Stick down writing/artwork on to an A4 sheet to make a great design! Use photocopies to make images bigger/smaller, cut round images . . . up to you. Chop typed bits into shorter sections to fit the shapes too! Remember to add page numbers at the bottom of each page!

ADVERTISING ED

Adverts bring in money to cover the cost of printing/ photocopying. Ask if teachers, parents or local businesses would like to place an ad in the mag. Set prices at maybe £5 for a quarter of a page, £10 for a half and £20 for a full page?

You can also organize competitions and ask local shops to donate prizes . . . if you mention who donated the choccy/books/paints, that's free publicity for the company, so many will be happy to help. Give it a go!

The advertising ed can also work with the art ed to make publicity posters and create a buzz about the mag!

GOING TO PRINT...

All the pages are in, laid out, illustrated and checked for mistakes. Everything has been signed off, publicity posters are up . . . you just need to print it!

Decide how many copies you think you can sell. How many kids are in the school? Are they keen? Will teachers and parents buy copies too? Ask a teacher/adult for advice.

A friendly teacher/librarian can ask the school office to photocopy your pages or arrange for them to be printed in the school repro department. Few schools would refuse!

Allow plenty of time to sort pages in the right order and staple together!

ON SALE!

Sell your mag from a playground stall, a table outside the office, even class to -class. Watch as the buzz spreads around the school . . . then celebrate! You did it!!!!

cathy cassidy's Best Friends' Day

When:
Saturday 4 July

What:
Cathy Cassidy's National Best Friends Day

Where:
EVERYWHERE!

Who:
EVERYONE!

The idea is very simple – **4 July** is the perfect opportunity to spend time with your best friends and show them just how much you care. It's a day to **celebrate friendship** and to share some good times together. It's a day for **fun, laughter, smiles** and **cakes**!

There will be **lots of events** happening up and down the country in **schools, bookshops** and **libraries,** but why don't you organize your own celebrations with your friends? Let's get the party started!

Show your **BFs** how much you care by organizing something that you could do together. The most **important thing** is **spending time with each other** and **having fun**!

Check out the next few pages for loads of **ideas** on hosting your own **National Best Friends Day party, yummy cake recipes,** instructions for how to make **dream flags** and even some **Random Acts of Kindness**.

Party, Party!

So what exactly will you do to celebrate? There are so many ideas and possibilities. Make your dreams come true ...

Throw a mini-party for your best friends

You could all watch a DVD together, or make your own dream flags to hang in your room. Or maybe you could bake your own Angel Cakes! (Try the delicious recipes coming up.) You could hold your party during the day, or you could use the opportunity to have a fab sleepover, with cool activities planned for the evening.

Hold a cake sale

Once you've baked yummy cakes with your friends, why not set up a stall to sell them? Maybe you could raise money for a charity that really means something to you?

Spend some time with your best friend

You could take the day to enjoy some quality time with your best friend. Go and do some of the things that you like doing together the most, whether that's shopping, going swimming, visiting the park, eating cakes in a bakery, reading books or *Mizz* together, looking at celeb gossip or just having a chat.

31

Do something for faraway friends

If you have a best friend who doesn't live near you, then this could be the time to do something special for them. You could put together a package of goodies for them as a treat or you could try to meet up with them for the day. Even just making the time to call them will make them smile!

Invite your friends to a clothes-swapping party

You might not be in love with that sparkly top any more, but maybe one of your friends would look great in it. And you'll all save money by not having to buy new clothes! Why not make it into a makeover party and spoil each other with some new hair looks?

Organize a picnic in the park

Make some little sandwiches, bake some cakes and buy some snacks, then invite your friends for a summer picnic in the park. You could organize some fun games like rounders, an egg and spoon race and hula hooping, or even just take along a frisbee for everyone to play with. Don't forget a blanket for everyone to sit on, and some sunscreen and hats if it's a sunny day.

Lay on a pamper party

Use 4 July to throw a really relaxing pamper party for your friends. Ask everyone to bring their most sensational outfits, and get glammed up together! Try shoulder massages, foot spas, nail art and hair braiding for a completely chilled-out treat.

Funny fancy dress

Laughing with your friends is the best thing in the world so set up a fancy-dress party for you and your BFs. Choose a funny theme to keep you all giggling, like animals, vegetables or celebs, or even dressing up as each other. Make your costumes together and laugh all day long!

Hold Your Own Friendship Festival

One of the coolest things about being an author is getting the chance to meet my readers! It's fab to take my VW camper van to bookshops, libraries, schools and festivals, and that's how the Cathy Cassidy Friendship Festivals evolved. Friendship is something worth celebrating, so why not use some of these ideas to put on your own Friendship Festival for National Best Friends Day?

CC x

Getting ready:

★ Send all your friends invitations telling them where and when the Friendship Festival is happening

★ You could ask everyone to dress up for the event and maybe award a small prize for the best outfit at the end

On the day:

★ Set the scene by decorating the venue with brightly coloured streamers and balloons

★ You could start by announcing the start of the Friendship Festival and explaining how Cathy tours the country with her van

★ Gather everyone together and read an extract from one of Cathy's books

★ Friendship bracelets are great fun to make. All you need to do is buy some brightly coloured thread from a department store and then plait three strings together.

★ There are lots of other things you can do to make your Friendship Festival really special, such as hair-braiding, funky music, make-overs, nail art, T-shirt customizing, competitions, sleepovers and lots of other craft activities. Mainly, just have lots of fun with your friends!

Angel Cake Heaven

GET YOURSELF:

2 ¼ cups plain flour
1 ⅓ cups sugar
2 large free-range eggs
3 tsp baking powder
½ tsp salt
½ cup butter/margarine
1 cup milk
1 tsp vanilla essence

FOR THE CHOCOLATE ICING:

150g butter – softened
250g icing sugar
2 tbsp cocoa powder
2 tbsp very hot water
Chocolate buttons or your favourite sweets

 Preheat your oven to 180°C/350°F/Gas Mark 4. Put paper cases in the cupcake tray.

 Put the flour, sugar, baking powder and salt into a large bowl. Mix well.

 Add the butter, milk and vanilla. Beat for 1 minute until thick and gooey, and add eggs. Beat for a further 1 minute on medium speed then 2 minutes on high speed.

 Spoon cupcake mix into tray until ½ to ⅔ full and bake for 20–25 minutes. Leave to cool on a cooling rack.

 For the icing, beat together the butter and icing sugar. Mix the cocoa powder and water in a separate bowl.

 Add the combined cocoa powder and water to the butter and sugar, beat until smooth and creamy then swirl over your angel cakes. Decorate with choccy buttons or any sweets to make your own delicious angel cake treats.

YUM!

Created by
 Candy Cakes

34

Finn's Fantastic
Choc 'n' Orange Cupcakes

GET YOURSELF:

A cupcake tray and paper cases
60g milk choccy
90g softened butter
225g brown sugar
2 free-range eggs
1 tsp grated orange rind
155ml orange juice
80g self-raising flour
2 tbsp cocoa powder

FOR THE TASTY TOPPING:

250g icing sugar
150g softened butter
2 tbsp cocoa powder
2 tsp hot water
Coloured sprinkles

 Preheat the oven to 175°C/340°F/Gas Mark 4, and place the cases in the tray.

 Take a small saucepan and add the grated orange rind, juice and chocolate. Stir over a low heat until it's smooth and melted, then leave to cool for a minute.

 Put the butter, eggs and sugar in a bowl and beat with an electric mixer until it's all fluffy.

 Using a sieve, sift the cocoa and flour into the fluffy butter mixture, then add the orange and chocolate mix. Give it a good stir.

 With a teaspoon place equal amounts of the mixture into the cupcake cases and bake for 25 minutes. Leave to cool.

 For the topping, beat the butter and icing sugar together. Combine the cocoa powder and water, and add to the buttery mixture. Beat until it's all soft and smooth, and swirl over the cupcakes. Add sprinkles – and eat!

Indigo's Blueberry Muffins

GET YOURSELF:

A muffin baking tray and paper cases
300g plain flour
2 tsp baking powder
250g blueberries
2 free-range eggs, lightly beaten
75g caster sugar
110g unsalted butter, melted
½ tsp vanilla extract
250ml full-fat milk

 Preheat the oven to 190°C/375°F/Gas Mark 5 and put the paper cases in the tray.

 Beat together the eggs, sugar, milk, melted butter and vanilla extract in a bowl until soft and fluffy.

 Now sift the flour and baking powder into the bowl and mix it all together, before carefully stirring in the blueberries.

 With a teaspoon, divide the mixture equally among the paper cases. Bake for 20–25 minutes or until the muffins have risen and are pale golden-brown.

Cathy's
Sticky Caramel Cupcakes

GET YOURSELF:

A cupcake tray and paper cases
1 free-range egg – lightly beaten
40g self-raising flour
125g plain flour
155ml milk
80g golden syrup
145g brown sugar
140g butter
100g dark chocolate

FOR THE TASTY TOPPING:

2 tsp hot water
2 tbsp cocoa powder
250g icing sugar
150g softened butter
Chopped nuts
Chocolate chips

 Preheat the oven to 170°C/340°F/Gas Mark 4 and put the paper cases in the tray.

 Take a small saucepan and add the butter, choccy, sugar, syrup and milk, and stir over a low heat until melted. Leave to cool for 15 minutes.

 Take a bowl and sift the plain flour and self-raising flour into it. Then add this flour to the caramel mix and stir in the egg. Mix until it's just combined.

 Spoon the cupcake mix into the tray in equal amounts and bake for 30 minutes. Leave to cool on a cooling rack.

 For the topping, beat the butter and sugar together. Combine the cocoa powder and water, and add to the buttery mixture. Beat until it's all soft and smooth and swirl over the cupcakes. Add chopped nuts and chocolate chips – now enjoy!

Scarlett's Scrumptious
Banana Walnut Muffins

GET YOURSELF:

3 bananas
A muffin baking tray and paper cases
145g walnuts, chopped
45ml buttermilk
1½ tsp bicarbonate of soda
110g wholemeal flour
110g plain flour
110g melted butter
2 free-range eggs
70g brown sugar
100g caster sugar

 Preheat the oven to 180°C/355°F/Gas Mark 4.
Place the paper cases in the tray.

 Mash up the bananas in a mixing bowl and add
the caster sugar, eggs and brown sugar. Stir them
all together.

 Add the melted butter and sift in the bicarbonate
of soda, plain flour and wholemeal flour. Stir
again, before adding the walnuts and buttermilk.
Mix it all up until just softened.

 Spoon the mix evenly into the paper cases and
bake for 20 minutes. Leave to cool on a cooling
rack and then munch away!

Cat's Crazy
Carrot Muffins

GET YOURSELF:

A muffin baking tray and paper cases
55g melted butter
2 free-range eggs
100g shredded carrot
225ml milk
1 tsp baking powder
60g brown sugar
100g raisins
125g plain flour
125g wholemeal flour

 Preheat the oven to 190°C/375°F/Gas Mark 5. Place the paper cases in the tray.

 Put the wholemeal flour, plain flour, sugar, raisins and baking powder in a large bowl. Stir them all together until well mixed.

 Mix the rest of the ingredients in a smaller bowl, before adding to the large bowl and stirring it all up.

 Spoon the mix evenly into the muffin tray and bake for 20 minutes. Leave to cool on a cooling rack before discovering how many you need to eat before you can see in the dark!

Cathy Cassidy's Dream Flags

Wishes and dreams are just other words for positive thinking, and that's something that can be very powerful!

The idea of **making dreams come true** is an important part of many of my books . . . In *Scarlett* the main character ties red ribbons on to a 'wishing tree'; in *GingerSnaps* Ginger wishes for a friend; and in *Driftwood* Paul creates his own kind of beach magic . . . Crazy? I don't think so!

So how can you make your wishes and dreams come true? Get together with some friends and create some beautiful **dream flags** to start the **magic** off . . . by writing down the dream you're creating really positive energy.

> **Dream flags** are inspired by the beautiful **Buddhist prayer flags** I first saw in Nepal . . . Buddhist prayer flags are made of brightly coloured cloth with **prayers** and **good-luck symbols** written on to them and they are draped around temples and holy places. The idea is that the wind catches the prayer and takes it to the four corners of the earth . . . Cool, huh?

So what are you waiting for?

You will need:

A3 white or coloured paper

Coloured crayons, felt pens, oil pastels, water-based paints, brushes, scissors, glue, glitter, sequins, yarn, foil streamers, tinsel, stickers, stars, tissue paper, ribbon, gold/silver pens and assorted collage materials

A long length of string/coloured cord/ribbon

IMAGINATION!!

How to make your DREAM FLAG:

 Take your piece of A3 paper and cut it in half lengthways. Then fold each piece in half so you have two long thin strips of paper. This will give you two flags.

 Use paints, pens, crayons, pastels or a combination of these to pattern/colour the paper. Or collage your flag with ribbon, foil, stars and paper!

Write your dream on to the flag-shape. If you'd rather keep the dream secret, just decorate the flag with patterns and symbols, but think about your dream while you are doing this.

 Use both sides of the flag, or get your friend to use one side so you can share the dream flag!

Fold your flag over the string/cord and staple or glue your flag into place . . . then hang the completed string of dream flags along a wall or classroom!

Dream it . . . then do it!

Random Acts
of Kindness

What is a random act of kindness?

It's hard to be specific, but when you are at the receiving end of a **RAOK** it makes your day. It's when someone does something unexpected, thoughtful or helpful – something that's not selfish.

National Best Friends Day on **4 July** is the perfect time to try out some **RAOK**s with your friends. Maybe you could do something lovely for one of your BFs, or maybe you could do something kind for someone else together. It's all about **spreading the message of friendship** and trying to **help people** who need it.

You can plan your **RAOK** in advance or just be spontaneous and help someone out of the blue. You'll feel great for doing it and your recipient will love it – everyone will get a **warm fuzzy feeling**!

You can even try an **environmentally friendly random act of kindness**, like removing a plastic bag from a pond so the wildlife in the area won't become entangled in it or picking up a drinks can and recycling it.

Copy cool Sam Taylor from *GingerSnaps* and try a random act of kindness everyday. Here are a few to start you off ...

★ Wash up without being asked

✦ Hug a friend!

★ Talk to someone who's feeling lonely or left out

★ Compliment a classmate on his/her appearance

✦ Send a card to your BF for no reason at all

★ Give a slice of pizza to the delivery man

★ If you get some small change from a shop, put it in their charity box

✦ Carry shopping for an elderly neighbour

★ Play with your little bruv/sister – it's fun!

★ Make your own little notepads from scrap paper and give them to people

✦ Give up your seat on the bus for someone else

★ Bake cupcakes or cookies and give them to someone as a treat

★ Send a book anonymously to a friend that you think they might like

✦ SMILE – it's free, and it makes everyone feel good. Especially you!

For the chance of receiving a Random Act of Kindness, go to your local Waterstone's store on Saturday 4 July. There will be some very special treats for lucky readers throughout the day. Check local stores for details.

Enjoy a Random Act of Kindness on us!

Waterstone's

If you love
cathy cassidy
then you'll love

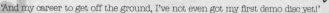

'Wacky, crazy, cool . . . you'll love it!' *Cathy Cassidy*

Maggi Gibson

Seriously Sassy

**'Right now boys are NOT part of my life plan.
I've got more than enough to do as it is.'**

'Yeah, like the planet to save,' Cordelia says dreamily.

'And my career to get off the ground, I've not even got my first demo disc yet!'

Sassy Wilde's had enough of pollution and Paradiso's plastic bags – she wants to make a difference. It's time to grab her guitar and start spreading some eco love . . .

But first she has to get round her mum and dad – officially the most embarrassing parentals In. The. World.

And it's not just endangered creatures keeping Sassy awake at night. Why, oh WHY, did Magnus (the Magnificent) offer her a bite of his muffin in biology?

WANT TO KNOW MORE? GET SASSY AT
seriouslysassy.co.uk

BEST FRIENDS are there for you in the good times and the bad. They can keep a secret and understand the healing power of chocolate.

BEST FRIENDS make you laugh and make you happy. They are there when things go wrong, and never expect any thanks.

BEST FRIENDS are forever,

BEST FRIENDS ROCK!

cathy cassidy's
My Best Friend Rocks!
enter at
cathycassidy.com
mizz
award

IS YOUR BEST FRIEND ONE IN A MILLION?
Go to **cathycassidy.com**
to see this year's winning entries.

In association with

 & **mizz**

Cathy Cassidy
Quiz Time

Are you Cathy's number one fan? Test your knowledge of all things Cathy with this quiz – and if you get all ten answers correct, treat yourself to a cupcake and blow yourself a kiss in the mirror!

 1. The title of Cathy's first book is:

A *Feverish*

B *Dizzy*

C *Sore Throat and High Temperature*

 2. When Hannah first meets Joey in *Driftwood*, is Joey wearing:

A Reindeer antlers?

B A tu-tu?

C A tiara?

 3. What is Indigo's favourite hobby?

A Drawing

B Daydreaming

C Dancing

  4. What is the name of the school that Scarlett gets expelled from?

A Bluehill Academy

B Redmount Academy

C Greenhall Academy

5. In *Sundae Girl*, what is Jude's mum's job?
   A Actress
   B Hairdresser
   C Singer

6. In *Lucky Star*, what is Mouse's real name?
   A Max
   B Michael
   C Martin

7. Where does Ginger's eleventh birthday party take place?
   A The ice rink
   B The swimming pool
   C The local pizzeria

8. In *Love, Peace and Chocolate*, what instrument does Jess play?
   A Flute
   B Guitar
   C Saxophone

9. What is the name of Cathy Cassidy's mad hairy lurcher?
   A Kelpie
   B Arnie
   C Stanley

10. Which magazine did Cathy work at for twelve years as an agony aunt?
   A *Holler*
   B *Shout*
   C *Squeal*

Right then, it's time to find out just how well you know Cathy and her books! We hope you didn't take a sneaky peek at the answers during the quiz . . .

Answers: 1. (b); 2. (a); 3. (b); 4. (c); 5. (b); 6. (b); 7. (c); 8. (a); 9. (a); 10. (b).

Have you ever had a crush? Fallen out with your best friend? Cathy Cassidy is here for you.

There are no questions that Cathy hasn't been asked or isn't afraid to answer, from **growing-up** to **dating**, **making friends**, **following your dreams** and **much more**.

Through the happy times, the mad and crazy times, and the days when you simply find yourself asking **'Why?'** – whatever's bugging you, **Cathy can help** . . . Here's an extract from her new book *Letters to Cathy*, coming in October.

Friends Forever?

Friendship is one of the most important things in our lives. It's the glue that sticks us together through good times and bad. A real friend will be there for you through the best and the worst of times: loyal, caring, thoughtful, fun.

Good friends are a little like family, and a best friend can often be the person who knows and understands you best in the world.

So, are friends forever? Well, sometimes. At this stage in your life, you're growing up, changing, working out who you really are . . . and sometimes, that means outgrowing old friends. It can take luck, hard work and effort on both sides to keep a friendship strong. And sometimes, no matter what you do, things fall apart . . .

Making Friends . . .

Dear Cathy,
My friends all went to different secondary schools and I'm struggling to make friends. I need help fast!
Tammi, age 11 x

Cathy,
I'm going to be moving to a new high school in the middle of the term, miles away from my old school and friends. I'm dreading it. Everyone will know each other and I know I'll never fit in . . .
Sumayya, age 13 x

To make new friends, you have to be friendly! You have to take a risk, make an effort, try talking to people you may not know very well. Smile, chat, ask questions, give compliments, listen, support . . . and make it a part of who you are. You'll soon make new contacts, and slowly, from there, new friendships may develop.

If, like Tammi, you're struggling, try mixing things up a little. Rather than rely on her classmates, Tammi should look further afield – join lunchtime clubs or after-school groups. She should choose a club or group that interests her – drama, art, sport, athletics, dance, debating, maths, music, whatever. That way, she'll be meeting people she already has something in common with. Working on something together, whether it's a play, a concert or a netball match, brings people together and breaks the ice. Tammi wants some close friends, but true friendship takes time to develop. She needs to be patient . . . those new friends are out there!

Starting a new school mid-term, like Sumayya, is not easy, but it can be a great way to meet new mates! She may not enjoy being the centre of attention, but her new classmates will be curious and interested, and most will want to make her welcome. Sumayya will have to take a deep breath and make sure she sees the change of school as an opportunity to make new friends, not a disaster that is ruining her life. She may not have chosen this, but it's happening – and her best option is to accept that and make the most of it.

So how do you make new mates? For some people it's easy, for others a nightmare . . . but one thing's for sure, if you're feeling lonely, you need to get out there and make some new connections.

Why do some people collect new mates the way the rest of us collect zits and split ends? Watch those people and you'll see that they have skills that literally attract others to them!

* They are open, confident and friendly.
* They smile!
* They are kind, supportive and generous.
* They are genuinely interested in others.
* They take time to chat about anything and everything.
* They give and receive compliments easily.
* They remember names and details.
* They are enthusiastic!
* They are upbeat, positive and fun to be around.
* They are interesting . . . they have things to talk about!
* They are not afraid to make plans . . . and include others in them.

Maybe those are qualities we could all work on having!

All the questions you EVER wanted to ask . . . answered by Cathy Cassidy. *Letters to Cathy* – OUT IN OCTOBER.

Friendships don't stay strong all by themselves ... you have to work at it! Sign up to our fab **Friendship Charter** and be a great mate ...

THE FRIENDSHIP CHARTER: 6 EASY STEPS TO MAKING A DIFFERENCE

I promise to show — and tell — my friends how much they mean to me. Often!

I promise to always listen and be there for my friends ... through thick and thin.

I promise to hug the people I care about and take time out to have fun with them!

I promise never to knowingly hurt a friend.

I promise to do one random act of kindness every day (even if it's just the washing up!).

I promise to speak out if I see someone being bullied — and make an effort to be friendly to the victim too.

Join other Cathy Cassidy fans and sign up to the **Cathy Cassidy Friendship Charter** officially at

cathycassidy.com

In association with

Follow your dreams with all cathy cassidy's gorgeous books

A delicious new story from Cathy Cassidy!

Anya used to dream of moving to Britain to start a brand-new life. But as she sits in a school where nobody understands her, she dreams of Polish summer skies and the place where she once belonged.

Then Anya meets bad boy Dan. He's no angel, but she's sure there's a sweeter side to him. And when things fall apart at school, Anya realizes she's not alone – how can Dan be such bad news when being with him feels like heaven?

Get your copy now!

puffin.co.uk